A gift for

From

Talk to the Tail

'cause the whiskers ain't listenin'!

by Oliver Christianson, a.k.a, Revilo

Copyright © 2003
Hallmark Licensing, Inc.

Published by Hallmark Books, a division of Hallmark Cards, Inc.,
Kansas City, MO 64141
Visit us on the Web at www.Hallmark.com.

Editor: Jane-Elyse Pryor and Todd Hafer
Designed by: Dan Horton
Cover design by: Wale' Adeniran
Art Director: Mark Cordes

Printed and bound in China
BOK 2039

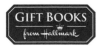

For:
Sylvia and Zoë

What other famous cartoonists say about Oliver and his work:

Revilo is one of the legends among cool cartoonists.
His drawings are the inspired ink carvings of a man up to his eyeballs
in talent; his writing belies a psyche on a permanent road trip
with unlimited beer. I dig this guy's work. Piraro

With Revilo, you're in the hands of a master!!!
There's always something profound about his work...This book is
funny in a way that runs deep!! John Callahan

Grrr! Ruff! Ruff! Peep! Peep! Meow! Meow! Bad Kitty! Great
and funny! Benita Epstein

This book is proof that Oliver Christianson should be looked upon
as a moral compass by the citizens of this great nation...
Nay-the world! Randy Rider

I loved Revilo's cartoon book about pets, but my dog was really offended.   Barbara Dale

People tell me Oliver is rude, insulting, and desperate...but to me, he's always been the opposite...desperate, insulting, and rude. Jeff Keane, Family Circus

Oliver Christianson is to cartooning what Dom DeLuise is to hang gliding...   Steve McGarry, National Cartoonist Society President

Oliver is a lot like pet hair - always sticking to your pants, except you can't lift him off with a lint roller. Rick Kirkman, Baby Blues

Talk to the Tail
'cause the whiskers ain't listenin'!

SECRET DOGGiE THOUGHTS

"THAT BETTER NOT BE MY WATCH."

Palm Beach resident walking
the world's smallest dog.

"DON'T LIE TO ME, YOU'RE DRAGGING YOUR FOOT, I CAN FEEL IT!"

...AND NOW, OUR NATIONAL ANTHEM AS BARKED BY LASSIE.

Edgar would ultimately regret
taking seduction advice
from his dog, Ranger.

"HEY! STUPID! IT'S THE CATS **ACROSS** THE STREET! WE HAVE A LITTLE DOOR AND CAN GO IN AND OUT ANYTIME WE WANT! HA-HA-HA!"

PASSING

"In the coming year, I resolve to
curb my obsession with parakeets."

" WHAT I HEAR YOU SAYING IS : 'QUACK! QUACK! QUACK!'"

"I THINK YOU KNOW VERY WELL <u>WHO</u>, MR. SCREECH OWL, IF THAT <u>IS</u> YOUR REAL NAME!"

DECORATIVE CAT TAIL COVERS

FLOCKED

KNIT WITH POM-POM

CHECKERED

SHAG

REVILO

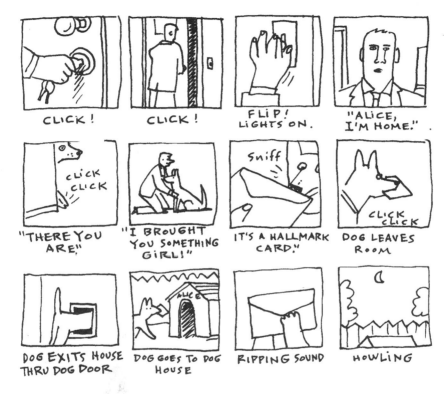

REJECTED STORYBOARD
FOR HALLMARK COMMERCIAL

A CAT DiSGUiSED AS A POODLE.

REViLo

15-POUND CAT IN A
SIZE 5½ SHOE BOX.

Lady →

Her Owner →

REVILO

HOW TO TELL THE DIFFERENCE BETWEEN A YOUNG CAT AND AN OLD CAT:

THE FIRST CAT ON THE MOON

REVILO

CAT PEOPLE ARE FAIRLY EASY TO SPOT.

I SPEND A LOT OF TIME THINKING ABOUT YOU.

IT HELPS ME KILL TIME IN BETWEEN MEALS.

COPYCAT

CAT STAND-UP

FLUFFY SENDS A MESSAGE

SHORTLY BEFORE THE BiG CRASH

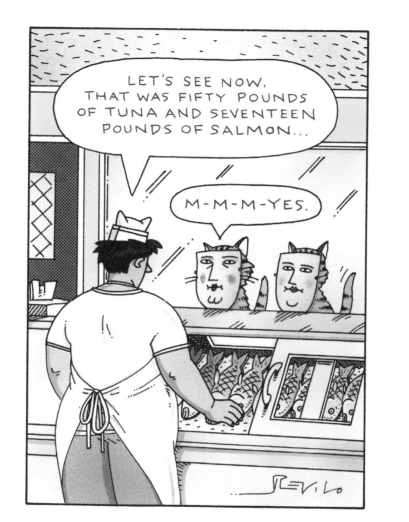

LITTLE KNOWN FACTS: A CAT WEIGHS TWICE

AS MUCH WHEN IT IS SLEEPING!

WE COULD CUT OUR HEATING COSTS BY 35%
IF EVERYONE SLEPT IN THEIR DRYER.

CAT LOVE

A CAT PLANNING OUT
ITS HOLIDAY SCHEDULE

HOW CATS COMMUNICATE:

When Cats Dream. . .

BEING A FIXED MALE HAS ITS MOMENTS...

BUT HE MANAGES TO SLEEP THROUGH THEM.

THE MIDNIGHT RIDER

AERIAL VIEW of THE TACKY CAT IN A SHOEBOX

A CAT MAP

THE TRADITIONAL HOLIDAY DINNER

WITH ALL THE TRIMMINGS (INCLUDING TACKY CAT)

TACKY CAT'S FAVORITE "METAL SCULPTURE"

THE "STARING AT THE
EMPTY BOWL" TRICK

TACKY CAT INSPECTING SIDEWALK.

THE RETURN of PUSS'N'CLOGS

DIRTY WATER IS ALWAYS MORE TASTY.

TACKY CAT HAVING A RELIGIOUS EXPERIENCE

...IN A NEW OIL SPOT ON THE DRIVEWAY.

CATS ARE TOUGH TO FOOL.

BUD AND DEB MAKE ARMPIT MUSIC
FOR THEIR CAT SYLVIA.

Our pets are laughing at us
behind our backs.

If you, or your pet, have enjoyed,
or been offended by, this book,
Hallmark would love to hear from you.
Please send your comments to:
Book Feedback
Hallmark Cards, Inc.
2501 McGee, Mail Drop 489
Kansas City, MO 64141-6580
Or e-mail us at
booknotes@Hallmark.com.